· Matt Silverman ·

Civil War
TRIVIA
QUIZ
BOOK

· Trivial Truths ·

· Matt Silverman ·

Civil War
TRIVIA
QUIZ
BOOK

· Trivial Truths ·

BARNES
&NOBLE
BOOKS
NEW YORK

The author thanks everyone who provided questions, corrections, and/or encouragement, especially Rick Campbell, Heather Russell, Billy MacKay, Sharon Bosley, and Dave Rasmussen.

Deborah, Max and Anna Silverman have endured years of useless trivia, map tidbits, and pointless detours. Thanks.

Dedication: For Lawrence F. Silverman, who shares my love of the Civil War.

Copyright © 2001 by Barnes & Noble, Inc.

ISBN: 0-7607-2587-X

Book Design by Lundquist Design, New York

Printed and bound in the United States of America

01 02 03 MP 9 8 7 6 5 4 3 2 1

OPM

I. A HOUSE DIVIDED AGAINST ITSELF

Q: What is the significance of the Mason-Dixon line?

Q: Of the approximately thirty million people living in America in 1860, how many lived in the South?

Q: What Yankee invention was the engine of the Southern economy?

Q: Which of these key mid-nineteenth century technologies were developed by Northerners: the steamboat, the telegraph, the revolver, the steel plow, the sewing machine?

Q: What was the size of the North's economic base relative to the South's?

A: To settle a boundary dispute, Charles Mason and Jeremiah Dixon partly surveyed the borderline between Pennsylvania and Maryland from 1763–1767. This became the popular name for the boundary between free and slave states.

A: About ten million, or one-third. Of these, about three and a half million, over one-third of the South's population, were slaves.

A: The cotton engine, or gin. Yale graduate Eli Whitney's 1793 invention led to the increase of cotton exports from less than one hundred tons per year when it was devised to over one million tons per year by 1850. Cotton was the South's major economic product, and the production of cotton was based on slave labor.

A: All of them.

A: The North's wealth was about nine times larger. The value of all Confederate manufactured goods was less than a quarter of that produced in New York alone.

Q: What is "States' Rights"?

Q: How many men fought in the Civil War?

Q: How many men died?

Q: How many were made prisoners of war?

Q: At the time of the Civil War, the Union had the largest army in the world, 1.5 to 2.2 million men. Who had the second largest army?

Q: Although comprising only one percent of the population of the North, African-Americans made up what percentage of the Union army at the war's end?

A: The concept, based on a strict interpretation of the Constitution, that all rights not specifically delegated to the Federal Government belong to the states. Among the rights that its proponents claimed were secession from the Union, nullification of federal laws, and the practice of slavery.

A: Estimates range from 3 to 3.8 million.

A: Approximately 600,000 men died—two percent of the total population, twenty percent of the combatants. This is more deaths than in any other American war. The Union army had over 350,000 dead, and the Confederates lost over 250,000.

A: About 214,000 Rebels were in Union prison camps; 26,000 died there. Nearly 194,000 Federals were in Confederate camps; 30,000 perished.

A: The Confederacy, with estimates in the range of 600,000 to 1.4 million soldiers.

A: By the end of the Civil War, ten percent of the Union army were black soldiers. Many of them were freed slaves from the Border States.

Q: What was the most horrific battle of the war?

Q: How many of the bloodiest battles did not take place in the South?

Q: What were the ten bloodiest battles?

A: Gettysburg, July 1–3, 1863. Over 51,000 men were killed, wounded, missing or captured, almost one-third of those who took part in the fighting. The Confederate army's victories up to this point was the "high water mark of the Confederacy," after which the tide clearly turned in the Union's favor.

A: Just two, Gettysburg and Antietam, both costly Union victories.

A: Casualty estimates vary. Among the deadliest battles were:
1. Gettysburg (Pennsylvania),
    July 1–3, 1863: 51,000 casualties.
2. Seven Days (Virginia),
    June 25–July 1, 1862: 36,000 casualties in several battles.
3. Chickamauga (Georgia),
    September 19–20, 1863: 35,000 casualties.
4. Chancellorsville (Virginia),
    May 1–4, 1863: 30,000 casualties.
5. Spotsylvania (Virginia),
    May 8–19, 1864: 27,000 to 30,000 casualties.
6. Antietam (Maryland),
    September 17, 1862: 26,000 casualties.
7. The Wilderness (Virginia),
    May 5–7, 1864: 25,000 to 30,000 casualties.
8. Second Bull Run (Virginia),
    August 29–30, 1862: 25,000 casualties.
9. Shiloh (Tennessee), April 6–7, 1862: 24,000 casualties.
10. Murfreesboro (Tennessee),
    December 31, 1862–January 3, 1863: 21,000 to 25,000 casualties.

Q: What general commanded troops in seven of the ten bloodiest battles?

Q: What was the profile of the typical Union and Rebel soldier?

Q: What Union politician had four brothers-in-law who fought for the South?

Q: In 1863, President Lincoln appeared before a secret morning session of the congressional Committee on the Conduct of the War. Why was he there and what did he testify?

A: Robert E. Lee was the Rebel commander at Gettysburg, Seven Days, Chancellorsville, Spotsylvania, Antietam, the Wilderness, and Second Bull Run.

A: Civil War soldiers, both Northern and Southern, were typically farmers, unmarried, between the ages of 18 and 29, white, native-born, and Protestant.

A: President Abraham Lincoln. Mary Todd Lincoln was from Lexington, Kentucky, and had many Confederate relatives.

A: The committee had been secretly investigating Lincoln's own wife as a possible Confederate spy. Because of her Southern roots and visits to the White House by Confederate sympathizers, Mary Todd Lincoln was suspected of disloyalty. Lincoln's testimony was terse and unequivocal: "I, Abraham Lincoln, President of the United States, appear of my own volition to say that I, of my own knowledge, know that it is untrue that any of my family holds treasonable communication with the enemy."

II. BLUE AND GRAY

Q: Who was the first casualty of abolitionist John Brown's raid on Harpers Ferry in October 1859?

Q: Who commanded the U.S. army troops that retook Harpers Ferry from Brown?

Q: What future Confederate commander led a contingent of Virginia Military Institute cadets to the scene of John Brown's hanging?

Q: What young actor was one of the militiamen present there?

Q: Which famous actor saved the life of Robert Todd Lincoln, the president's young son?

Q: With what luxuries did the elite 7th New York Regiment set out for Washington in April 1861?

II. BLUE AND GRAY

A: Hayward Shepherd, the town baggage master, who was a free black man.

A: Lieutenant Colonel Robert E. Lee.

A: Thomas Jackson, who would later be known as "Stonewall" Jackson.

A: John Wilkes Booth, later to become infamous as Lincoln's assassin.

A: Edwin Booth, a brother of Lincoln's assassin and one of the most well-known actors of his day. According to an account given by Robert Lincoln, after he lost his footing on a Jersey City, New Jersey train platform in 1863, Edwin Booth pulled him back to safety by his coat collar.

A: Sandwiches from Delmonico's and one thousand velvet-covered campstools on which to sit and enjoy them.

Q: Sometimes the Federals named battles after streams, the Rebels after towns. By what name did the Confederates refer to these battles?
   1. Antietam
   2. Bull Run
   3. Stone's River

Q: Who said, "Damn the torpedoes. Full speed ahead!"?

Q: Which state was his home?

Q: How many generals were killed or wounded at Antietam in September 1862?

Q: In the Seven Days Battles (June and July 1862), Union General Phillip St. George Cooke unsuccessfully chased Rebel J. E. B. "Jeb" Stuart's cavalry. What special tie connected them?

Q: For which side did Missouri send thirty-nine regiments to fight in the siege of Vicksburg?

A: 1. Sharpsburg.
   2. Manassas.
   3. Murfreesboro.

A: Union Admiral David G. Farragut, in Mobile Bay, August 1864.

A: The great Union admiral was from a landlocked Southern state, Tennessee.

A: Eighteen; three were killed and six were wounded from each side.

A: Cooke was Stuart's father-in-law.

A: Both. Seventeen for the Confederacy, twenty-two for the Union.

Q: Regiments of white soldiers went to fight for the North from which Confederate states?

Q: How many medals were awarded in the Confederate army during the war?

Q: How did Kentucky Senator John Crittendon's two sons distinguish themselves during the war?

Q: What garb did Northern newspapers report Confederate President Jefferson Davis was wearing when he was captured in Georgia after the war?

Q: What was the final land skirmish of the Civil War?

Q: Who was the last Rebel commander to surrender?

A: All of them except South Carolina.

A: None.

A: Both became major generals: Thomas Leonidas Crittendon for the North and George Bibb Crittendon for the South.

A: A dress. Although Northern newspapers spread this rumor energetically, the story is untrue. For disguise and protection, Davis was wearing a shawl.

A: The Battle of Palmito Ranch near Brownsville, Texas, on May 12, 1865. It was a Confederate victory.

A: Captain James I. Waddell of the raider, *Shenandoah*, burned unarmed Union whaling ships in June 1865, then sailed to England to surrender there.

III. ON THIS CONTINENT A NEW NATION

Q: What state stretches from south of Richmond (the Confederate capital) to north of Boston (the Union's northernmost big city)?

Q: Which of the southern states seceded first?

Q: Which of the southern states seceded last?

Q: Where was the first Confederate currency printed?

Q: What part of the South refused to secede from the Union and became its own state in 1863?

Q: Which of the eleven Confederate states was readmitted to the Union first?

Q: Which of the Confederate states was readmitted to the Union last?

Q: Only one southern city was among the twenty largest in the country in 1860. Which one?

III. ON THIS CONTINENT A NEW NATION

A: Illinois. Not surprisingly, its citizens were deeply divided during the Civil War.

A: South Carolina seceded on December 20, 1860.

A: Tennessee seceded on June 8, 1861.

A: In New York.

A: West Virginia was admitted to the Union on June 20, 1863.

A: Tennessee was readmitted on July 24, 1866, two years before most of the other states.

A: Texas wasn't readmitted until March 30, 1870. (Georgia was readmitted on June 25, 1868 and then readmitted a second time on July 15, 1870.)

A: New Orleans ranked sixth with 168,675 people. By contrast, New York had 813,669 (over a million if you include Brooklyn); Philadelphia had 565,529. The next largest southern city was Charleston, South Carolina (twenty-second) with 40,522.

Q: Which strategically important town changed hands more times than any other during the war?

Q: What was the first capital of the Confederacy?

Q: What were Confederate secret agents plotting in Chicago in 1864?

Q: What did Rebel agents do in St. Albans, Vermont on October 19, 1864?

Q: General William Tecumseh Sherman's troops punished one state even more harshly than they treated Georgia. Which state and why?

A: Winchester, Virginia alternated between Federal and Confederate control fifty to one hundred times, including at least one dozen formal changes of possession. Its location at the head of the Shenandoah Valley, the South's principal invasion route to the north, was critical.

A: Montgomery, Alabama. Richmond became the capital after Virginia seceded.

A: They attempted to free Rebel prisoners of war from Camp Douglas.

A: They robbed a bank, netting over $200,000.

A: Although General Sherman's "March to the Sea" in Georgia is still cited as one of the most savage onslaughts in American military history, his troops were even more vengeful in South Carolina. Because of the state's lead role in secession, many Northern soldiers regarded South Carolina as one of the main culprits of the war.

IV. THE PECULIAR INSTITUTION

Q: What was the "peculiar institution"?

Q: Under the Constitution, by what fraction was each slave to be counted?

Q: What was the Missouri Compromise?

Q: What was the name of William Lloyd Garrison's militant antislavery newspaper?

IV. THE PECULIAR INSTITUTION

A: Slavery.

A: For purposes of levying taxes and apportioning representation in Congress, a slave was counted as three-fifths of a person.

A: In 1820 Congress agreed to admit Missouri as a slave state and Maine as a free state. Slavery was prohibited in the vast territory of the Louisiana Purchase north of the Arkansas-Missouri border (except for Missouri).

A: *The Liberator.* The Massachusetts editor-publisher was one of the most effective advocates of nonviolent abolition. He opposed the Union war effort until the Emancipation Proclamation was issued.

Q: Who led a bloody slave uprising in Virginia in August 1831?

Q: What was the Dred Scott decision and what made it so important?

Q: What great abolitionist turned down John Brown's personal invitation to join the raid on Harpers Ferry?

Q: What were "fire-eaters"?

Q: What state first called for the enlistment of African-American troops in the Civil War?

A: Nat Turner and some sixty to eighty fellow slaves killed Turner's master and fifty-six other white victims. Federal troops responded by killing 100–200 slaves. Turner was among the seventeen slaves who were captured and hanged.

A: In 1857, the United States Supreme Court ruled that Dred Scott, a Virginia-born slave, could not be freed merely because he had previously lived in a free state. In the decision, written by Chief Justice Roger Taney, the court ruled that neither slaves nor their descendants could be citizens; and thus had no right to sue. They ruled also that the Missouri Compromise was unconstitutional. This pro-Southern decision infuriated Northern Republicans and helped lead to Lincoln's nomination.

A: Frederick Douglass, who later said of Brown's zeal, "Mine was as the taper light; his was as the burning sun."

A: The name given to the most extreme secessionists and proponents of slavery.

A: Rhode Island. The state also was the first to abolish slavery.

Q: In which Union states were African-Americans allowed to vote?

Q: Did Lincoln free the slaves?

Q: Did Lincoln fight the war because he wanted to end slavery?

Q: The Thirteenth Amendment to the Constitution finally abolished slavery. When was it ratified by the states?

Q: Why was lawyer John S. Rock's admission to practice before the Supreme Court on February I, 1865 so unusual?

Q: When the *Richmond Examiner* said in March 1865 that the Confederacy would "not deny General Lee anything he asks for," for what had he asked?

A: Only in Maine, Massachusetts, New Hampshire, and Vermont.

A: Sorta. The Emancipation Proclamation freed only those slaves in Arkansas, Texas, Mississippi, Alabama, Florida, Georgia, the Carolinas, and in parts of Louisiana and Virginia. However, Lincoln had no control over those areas when the proclamation was issued. Congress had already freed the slaves in D.C. and the West. Slaves in Maryland, Tennessee, and Missouri were still not released. Some slaves gained their freedom by enlisting. Many, of course, freed themselves by running away.

A: No. Lincoln said "My paramount object in this struggle is to save the Union and is not either to save or to destroy slavery."

A: Not until December 1865, eight months after Lincoln's death.

A: John S. Rock was the first black attorney to be admitted to argue cases before the U.S. Supreme Court.

A: He asked the Congress to arm slaves to fight for the South.

24

V. THE FIERY TRIAL THROUGH
WHICH WE PASS

Q: Which United States president had a descendant
that was taken hostage in John Brown's raid at
Harpers Ferry?

Q: What were the casualties in the Confederate
bombardment of Fort Sumter on April 12–13,
1861, the opening battle of the Civil War?

Q: What lavishly named Confederate general had
overall command of this attack?

Q: Major Robert Anderson, commander of the Union
outpost at Fort Sumter, had been an artillery
instructor at West Point. Which Confederate
general had been a brilliant student and an assistant
to him at the U.S. Military Academy?

Q: What young recruit had Anderson enlisted in the
Black Hawk War of 1832?

V. THE FIERY TRIAL THROUGH
WHICH WE PASS

A: One hostage was George Washington's great-grandnephew, Colonel Lewis Washington.

A: One Confederate horse died.

A: General Pierre Gustave Toutant Beauregard.

A: General Pierre Gustave Toutant Beauregard.

A: Abraham Lincoln. In this skirmish U.S. troops drove Native Americans under Chief Black Hawk across the Mississippi to inferior lands onto which they were forcibly resettled.

Q: Prominent Washington residents rode out to the First Battle of Bull Run in July 1861 with picnic baskets and binoculars, boldly expecting to see a Union rout. They witnessed a stunning Southern victory and Union "skedaddle." Where did the Rebels find New York Congressman Albert Ely?

Q: When the Union warship *San Jacinto* stopped the steamer *Trent* off the shore of Cuba and arrested two Confederate agents, a political crisis erupted. Why?

Q: What were the two ironclad ships that fought off the coast of Virginia in March 1862?

Q: What was the largest ironclad, which eventually surrendered in Mobile Bay in August 1864?

Q: What were the *Hattie, Banshee, Let Her Rip,* and *Lynx*?

Q: Which twin Federal victories in February 1862 fortified the Union position in Kentucky and middle and west Tennessee?

A: Hiding behind a tree.

A: The *Trent* was a British ship. The British prime minister was outraged at the seizure and sent 11,000 troops to Canada, on alert. Lincoln, fearing *another* war, freed the captives on Christmas Day 1861.

A: The Union's *Monitor* and the Confederacy's *Merrimack* clashed in the first battle of two ironclad ships. It was a draw.

A: A Confederate ship, the *Tennessee*.

A: They were a few of the thousands of Confederate vessels engaged in getting through the Union naval blockade of Confederate ports which lasted most of the war. Although many ships, called "runners," got in and out, the blockade helped cripple the Southern economy.

A: The Battles of Fort Henry and Donelson. These were Ulysses S. Grant's first great victories.

Q: What two-day battle in 1862 was larger and bloodier than any previous American battle?

Q: How did Union General George McClellan bring the huge Army of the Potomac to the Peninsular Campaign in the Spring of 1862?

Q: What did Confederate commander Richard S. Ewell lose at the Second Battle of Bull Run, August 28–30, 1862?

Q: What was the worst one-day bloodbath of the war?

Q: What was the name of the pacifist sect whose simple church was the scene of some of the fiercest fighting at Antietam?

Q: What was Confederate General John Bell Hood's poignant response when asked where his division was after they broke a Union assault at Antietam?

Q: Who was the Union commander at the Battle of La Glorieta Pass, New Mexico, in March 1862?

A: Shiloh cost about 24,000 casualties, including 3,477 dead, on April 6–7, 1862.

A: Instead of marching directly south from Washington, they sailed down the Potomac and Chesapeake Bay in an armada of 400 ships to Fort Monroe, Virginia, then marched up the York-James Peninsula.

A: Ewell lost a leg at Groveton, at the beginning of the Second Battle of Bull Run.

A: September 17, 1862, at Antietam. About 26,000 were killed, wounded or missing.

A: The Dunkers.

A: "Dead on the field."

A: Major John M. Chivington. Two years later he led troops in the notorious Sand Creek Massacre in Colorado.

Q: What obstacle halted the Federal advance at Fredricksburg, Virginia for two to three weeks in late November 1862?

Q: From which hills did Rebel artillery devastate the Union forces at Fredricksburg?

Q: What rare celestial phenomenon was witnessed after Fredricksburg?

Q: Prior to the Battle of Chancellorsville in May 1863, who said, "May God have mercy on General Lee, for *I* will have none"?

Q: Where was the greatest cavalry clash in American history?

Q: What was the largest battle to take place west of the Mississippi River?

Q: What civilian scout, employed by the Union army, kept General Curtis informed of the Confederate troop movements in the area where this battle took place?

A: The Rappahannock River. Led by General Ambrose Burnside, the Federal Army of the Potomac raced to Fredericksburg, only to have their advance grind to a halt on the eastern bank of the Rappahannock River, opposite the city. Burnside's campaign was delayed while they waited for pontoon bridges to be built so they could cross the river.

A: Marye's Heights. Wave after wave of Federal attackers were mowed down by Confederate troops—nine thousand Union soldiers were killed or wounded.

A: The Northern Lights, or aurora borealis. Rebel soldiers took it as a sign that God favored their victory.

A: General Joseph "Fighting Joe" Hooker, who lost 17,000 men there. Lee survived, but he suffered 13,000 casualties, including Stonewall Jackson.

A: At Brandy Station, Virginia, where 21,000 horsemen led by Confederate General Jeb Stuart and Union commander Alfred Pleasonton fought to a draw on June 9, 1863.

A. The Battle of Pea Ridge, in Arkansas in March 1862. Confederate Major General Earl Van Dorn led 16,000 soldiers against 10,000 Union soldiers, led by Brigadier General Samuel R. Curtis. It was a Union victory.

A. Twenty-five year old James Butler Hickok, later to be known as "Wild Bill" Hickok, the legendary gunfighter and lawman of the West.

VI. WAR IS HELL

Q: Which cities did Confederate General Robert E. Lee want to threaten by his move north in June 1863?

Q: When the Battle of Gettysburg began on July 1, 1863, how long had General George G. Meade been in command of the Federal Army of the Potomac?

Q: On the first day at Gettysburg (July 1, 1863), from which directions did the opposing armies approach each other?

Q: Whose failure to be Lee's "eyes and ears" at Gettysburg cost the Confederate general the intelligence he needed about Union positions?

VI. WAR IS HELL

A: Washington, Baltimore, and Philadelphia. After defeating the Union forces of General Joseph Hooker at Chancellorsville, Lee decided to invade the North to further discourage the enemy.

A: Four days. On June 28, 1863, President Lincoln appointed Meade to replace Hooker.

A: The North came from the south and the South came from the north (and west).

A: Jeb Stuart, who had not reported to his superior for days, arrived at Gettysburg too late to provide Lee with vital information on the positions of the Union forces.

Q: What bold and unusual maneuver did the 20th Maine perform in its defense of Little Round Top against a superior force?

Q: Along what ominously named crest were the Union forces deployed at Gettysburg?

Q: For what disastrous attack on the third day at Gettysburg did Lee apologize to the survivors?

Q: What happened to the University Greys in Pickett's Charge?

Q: What general, sometimes credited with the development of field fortifications, argued with Lee at Gettysburg and was right?

Q: Why was July 4, 1863 such an important Independence Day?

A: Realizing that the Confederate forces could turn the Union flank, the 20th Maine regiment scattered the Rebels with a bayonet charge.

A: Cemetery Ridge. Fifteen thousand Confederate troops assaulted Cemetery Ridge, held by about 10,000 Federal infantrymen in the military action known as Pickett's Charge.

A: Pickett's Charge, an infantry assault across a mile-long open field against superior Union positions on July 3, 1863.

A: Every man in this company of students from Ole Miss was killed or wounded.

A: Confederate General James Longstreet disagreed with Lee's strategy of attacking the Union forces on Cemetery Ridge.

A: Two important and prolonged battles ended that day. General Lee retreated from Gettysburg, Pennsylvania, after three days of bitter fighting, and General Grant finally captured Vicksburg, Mississippi, after the long siege. These two simultaneous and stunning Union victories sealed the South's defeat. (Vicksburg residents did not celebrate the Fourth of July again for eighty years.)

Q: Who surrendered to General Ulysses S. Grant after the Siege of Vicksburg in 1863?

Q: Why was Vicksburg strategically important for the Union?

Q: What took place in New York City in mid-July 1863?

Q: Who were the "Jayhawkers" and the "Bushwhackers"?

Q: William Clarke Quantrill was the most infamous of the Bushwhackers. What was his bloodiest raid?

A: Lieutenant General John C. Pemberton surrendered on the forty-eighth day. Civilians had resorted to living in caves and eating rats, dogs, and peabread, a mixture of ground peas, water, and salt.

A: It was the last major Confederate stronghold on the Mississippi River. The Union held New Orleans and Memphis, and the only other river city with a railroad was Vicksburg. The loss of Vicksburg divided the South, stopped supplies from coming through by rail, and gave the North control of the Mississippi River.

A: Violent anti-draft riots that left over 100 dead. Smaller riots took place that summer in other cities, including Boston.

A: Union and Confederate guerillas, respectively, who fought along the Kansas-Missouri border through much of the war.

A: On August 21, 1863, Quantrill and his raiders murdered at least 150 men and boys at an antislavery stronghold in Lawrence, Kansas.

Q: Which notorious outlaws were part of Quantrill's troop?

Q: What key Southern city fell to Union troops on September 2, 1863 and remained a Northern stronghold through the remainder of the war?

Q: One of the Union color-bearers at Missionary Ridge in November 1863 was Medal of Honor winner Arthur MacArthur, Jr. Who was his famous son?

Q: What was the first ship ever destroyed by a submarine?

Q: In what overgrown Virginia thicket did Confederate troops defeat Grant on May 5–7, 1864, a year after they had defeated Hooker there?

A: The James Brothers (Jesse and Frank) and the Younger Brothers.

A: Knoxville, Tennessee. Despite a valiant attack by Confederate General James Longstreet two months later, Knoxville remained in Northern hands. The Confederates called Union supporters from the Volunteer State "Tennessee Tories."

A: World War Two leader General Douglas MacArthur. (General George Patton's grandfather fought in Lee's Army of Northern Virginia.)

A: The Union sloop *Housatonic* was sunk by the *Hunley*, a Rebel submarine, on February 17, 1864. The explosion sunk the *Hunley*, also.

A: The Wilderness. Grant abandoned the area, realizing that mounting an attack was next to impossible.

Q: How was General James Longstreet wounded at the Wilderness?

Q: Who did General John B. Gordon force away from the front at the Battle of Spotsylvania Courthouse, in May 1864?

Q: What disastrous assault did General Grant admit was a mistake?

Q: The Confederate ship *Alabama* sunk dozens of Union vessels. What was its own fate?

Q: What Union general ordered his troops into a crater at Petersburg on July 30, 1864, where Confederate soldiers shot them like fish in a barrel?

Q: Also on July 30, 1864, Confederate General Jubal Early's cavalry blackmailed the town of Chambersburg, Pennsylvania for $100,000. What happened?

A: He was shot by his own sentries.

A: He and his men sent Robert E. Lee to the rear, fearing Lee would be shot by Union gunners.

A: His charge against dug-in positions at Cold Harbor, Virginia, on June 1, 1864. Seven thousand Union soldiers were shot in just over ten minutes.

A: The USS *Kearsarge* crippled it in the English Channel off Cherbourg, France on June 19, 1864.

A: General Ambrose Burnside. Lincoln said, "Only Burnside could have managed such a coup, wringing one last spectacular defeat from the jaws of victory."

A: Payment was refused, and the business district was burned down.

Q: Which general did Grant send to waste the Shenandoah Valley so that "crows flying over it for the balance of the season will have to carry their provender"?

Q: What city was captured shortly after the Battles of Peachtree Creek and Ezra Church?

Q: On Sherman's March to the Sea in the autumn of 1864, his men stopped at Milledgeville, Georgia and built bonfires with what item?

Q: What bloody charge cost General John Bell Hood his army?

Q: What Christmas gift did Sherman present to Lincoln in 1864?

Q: What battle broke the Confederate lines at Petersburg, leading to the loss of Richmond, and Lee's retreat to Appomattox?

A: Phillip H. Sheridan, in September 1864.

A: Atlanta, in September 1864, by William T. Sherman and his Grand Army of the West.

A: Stacks of Confederate currency.

A: The infantry charge at the Battle of Franklin in Tennessee on November 30, 1864. Six Confederate generals died there.

A: The city of Savannah, which he had captured on December 22, 1864, along with its heavy guns, ammunition, and huge stores of cotton.

A: Five Forks, on April Fool's Day, 1865.

Q: During which battle in Lee's retreat did he lose six generals?

Q: What Confederate general led the final charge of the Army of Northern Virginia?

Q: What was Colonel Ely Parker's job at Appomattox on April 9, 1865?

Q: What golden-haired Indian fighter was part of Grant's officer corps at Appomattox?

Q: What did Custer survive in 1867?

Q: Where were the following battles?
   1. The Hornets' Nest
   2. The Sunken Lane
   3. The Crater
   4. Bloody Lane
   5. The Battle Above the Clouds

Q: Who said, "War is hell"?

A: Six Confederate commanders, including George Washington Custis Lee, Robert E. Lee's son, were captured at Sayler's Creek, on April 6, 1865.

A: John B. Gordon, at Appomattox.

A: Colonel Ely Parker, a member of the Seneca tribe, was one of the military secretaries on General Grant's staff.

A: George Armstrong Custer, then a twenty-three year old Union general. Custer, famous for his reckless behavior and long ringlets, later died at the Battle of Little Bighorn in Montana in 1876.

A: A court martial for being absent from duty during the campaign against the Southern Cheyenne. He was suspended from duty for a year.

A: 1. Shiloh. 2. Gettysburg.
   3. Petersburg. 4. Antietam.
   5. Lookout Mountain.

A: General Sherman, speaking to the graduating class of the Michigan Military Academy in 1879 said, "There is many a boy here today who looks on war as all glory, but, boys, it is all hell."

VII. THE BRAVE MEN, LIVING AND DEAD

Q: What was the size of the standing army of the United States at the beginning of the Civil War?

Q: What percentage of the U.S. army officers went to fight for the South?

Q: How many Confederate generals were West Point graduates?

Q: How many Union generals had graduated from West Point?

Q: What were they doing before the war?
   1. Joshua L. Chamberlain, the hero of Little Round Top
   2. Confederate President Jefferson Davis
   3. Union General U. S. Grant
   4. Clara Barton
   5. Confederate General Joseph E. Johnston

Q: Jesse Grant, the father of future General and President U. S. Grant, once worked for the father of someone almost equally famous. Identify him.

VII. THE BRAVE MEN, LIVING AND DEAD

A: Fewer than 17,000 men, most of them stationed in the Far West.

A: Approximately one-third.

A: The South had 425 generals during the war. One hundred forty-six, or thirty-four percent, had graduated from West Point.

A: Two hundred seventeen of the 583 Union generals (thirty-seven percent) were West Point graduates.

A: 1. Rhetoric professor at Bowdoin College, Maine.
    2. Senator from Mississippi.
    3. Harness-maker's clerk.
    4. Patent office clerk.
    5. Quartermaster-general of the U.S. army.

A: While a teenager, Jesse Grant apprenticed at the Ohio tannery of Owen Brown, the father of violent abolitionist John Brown.

Q: What position was Robert E. Lee offered before the war started?

Q: Who was the head of the Union army at the beginning of the Civil War?

Q: Other than Winfield Scott, how many Union generals had ever commanded an army in the field prior to the Civil War?

Q: What politically named general was in charge of artillery batteries at Fort Sumter?

Q: Who was called "the Virginia Creeper?"

Q: What nicknames did he favor?

Q: What did General George B. McClellan do to follow up his victories in the Battles of the Seven Days in June and July 1862?

Q: What handsome Kentuckian did both Grant and Davis think was the best soldier in the Confederacy?

A: Lincoln asked him to command the Union army.

A: Winfield Scott, the seventy-five-year-old hero of the Mexican War.

A: One, John Wool, age seventy-seven, a veteran of the War of 1812.

A: General States Rights Gist. Any doubt which side he was on?

A: Union General George B. McClellan was famous for his timidity and earned this nickname as a result. Lincoln fired him twice (and defeated him for President in 1864).

A: McClellan preferred "Little Mac" or "Young Napoleon."

A: He retreated down the Peninsula to the safety of Union gunboats.

A: General Albert Sidney Johnston, who was killed at the Battle of Shiloh (April 6, 1862).

Q: How did Thomas Jackson get the nickname "Stonewall"?

Q: What did Stonewall Jackson call his fast-moving infantry in the Shenandoah Valley Campaign of 1862?

Q: What did Stonewall Jackson suck compulsively during battle?

Q: What were the names of these generals' favorite horses?
   1. Robert E. Lee
   2. Ulysses S. Grant
   3. George B. McClellan
   4. Phillip H. Sheridan
   5. Albert Sidney Johnston

Q: What was unique about the way Lee rode to Antietam?

Q: Where were Confederate Generals John Bell Hood and A. P. Hill during part of this ride to Antietam?

A: Several southern commands crumpled during the First Battle of Bull Run, July 21, 1861. General Bernard Bee rallied his own troops saying something like, "Look, there is Jackson with his Virginians, standing like a stone wall!" The lines held and the name stuck, but Bee was killed shortly thereafter.

A: "Foot cavalry." They marched almost 400 miles in about a month.

A: Lemons.

A: 1. Traveller.
2. Cincinnati.
3. Daniel Webster.
4. Rienzi.
5. Fire-eater.

A: Both his hands were bandaged and splinted after a fall.

A: At the rear, under arrest after quarreling with their superiors.

Q: What did a lucky Union soldier find wrapped around three cigars just before Antietam?

Q: How did Stonewall Jackson die?

Q: What blacksmith's son made a fortune selling land, cotton, and slaves, and became a general?

Q: With which group did the blacksmith's son later play a key role?

Q: Who was Stand Watie?

Q: Union General John Pope frequently said that his headquarters were in the saddle. What did his detractors say?

A: A copy of Lee's orders. Even with that intelligence, McClellan refused to move forward boldly; had he done so, he might have hastened the end of the war.

A: He was shot accidentally by his one of his own men at Chancellorsville, May 2, 1863, and died shortly thereafter from complications.

A: Nathan Bedford Forrest. A brilliant cavalry officer, he was said to have had thirty horses shot from under him during the war.

A: Forrest was a founder and Grand Wizard of the Ku Klux Klan.

A: The highest-ranking Native American in the Rebel army. Watie was a brigadier general who was largely responsible for the Cherokee alliance with the Confederacy.

A: They said his headquarters were where his hindquarters should be.

VIII. THE LAST FULL MEASURE OF DEVOTION

Q: What was Ulysses S. Grant's real name?

Q: William Tecumseh Sherman used his real name. Who was Tecumseh?

Q: Grant's penchant for whiskey is legendary. Did he have other vices?

Q: Name the men who had headed the Union army prior to Lincoln's appointment of Grant as the commander in chief in 1864.

Q: Which old friends from before the war tragically faced each other's forces at the Angle in Gettysburg?

Q: Who was "the Rock of Chickamauga"?

VIII. THE LAST FULL MEASURE OF DEVOTION

A: Hiram Ulysses Grant. Official papers at West Point tagged him with "Ulysses Simpson" Grant, and it stuck. Later, he was sometimes called "Unconditional Surrender" Grant.

A: Tecumseh was a Chief of the Shawnee Tribe, and a noted military leader, who fought with the British against the United States during the War of 1812. He died in battle in 1813.

A: During the second day of the Wilderness, he is reported to have smoked twenty-four cigars. He often smoked twenty a day and was described as smoking coolly under fire.

A: Winfield Scott, Irvin McDowell, George B. McClellan, John Pope, McClellan (a second time), Ambrose Burnside, Joseph Hooker and George Gordon Meade.

A: Union General Winfield Scott Hancock and Confederate General Lewis A. Armistead, who was killed there.

A: Although it was a Rebel victory, Union General George Henry "Pap" Thomas held his ground during the Battle of Chickamauga.

Q: For which Union general is a tonsorial style named?

Q: Who was the youngest Union general?

Q: Who was known as "the Fighting Bishop"?

Q: Which rear admiral scuttled the Confederate fleet in the James River when Richmond fell in April 1865?

Q: What Union officer later accepted the surrenders of Native American leaders Geronimo and Chief Joseph?

Q: What Confederate officer was executed after the war's end for his actions during the war?

A: "Sideburns" are a play on the name of General Ambrose Burnside, famous for his extravagant muttonchop whiskers.

A: Galusha Pennypacker, born in Valley Forge, was promoted to general at the age of twenty in February 1865.

A: General Leonidas Polk was known as Louisiana's Fighting Bishop because, in addition to his military rank, he was an Episcopal Bishop. Neither title kept him from a tragic death: On June 14th, 1864, he was killed by artillery fire while observing Northern positions at Pine Mountain, Georgia.

A: Raphael Semmes, who commanded the Confederate navy in the James River.

A: Nelson A. Miles, who began his military career in the Civil War. In the 1870s and 1880s, he led successful campaigns against Native American tribes. In 1895, he was named Commanding General of the U.S. Army.

A: After the war, Captain Henry Wirz, commander of the Andersonville Prison, was tried and convicted by a U.S. military commission for the deplorable conditions at the prison. He was hanged on November 10, 1865.

Q: Who were the following?
1. Old Abe
2. Old Brains
3. Old Blue Light
4. Old Rosy
5. Old Pete
6. Old Baldy
7. Old Woodenhead
8. Old Beeswax
9. Old Fuss and Feathers
10. Old Jube

Q: What was John Wilkes Booth's original plan for Lincoln?

Q: Who else was to be assassinated after Booth's plans changed?

A: 1. President Abraham Lincoln.
    2. West Point tactician and Union General,
       Henry W. Halleck.
    3. Stonewall Jackson, because of the way his eyes
       lit up in battle.
    4. Union General William Rosecrans.
    5. Confederate Lt. General James Longstreet
       (a.k.a. "Lee's
       Old War Horse").
    6. Confederate General Richard S. Ewell.
    7. Confederate General John Bell Hood.
    8. Confederate Admiral Raphael Semmes, known
       for his wild moustache.
    9. Pomp-and-circumstance loving General
       Winfield Scott.
    10. Confederate General Jubal Early
        (a.k.a. "Jubilee").

A: He wanted to kidnap Lincoln and take him to
    Richmond for a prisoner-of-war exchange. When
    the war ended, he changed his plan to assassinating
    the president.

A: Vice President Andrew Johnson, Secretary of State
    William Seward (who was stabbed seriously but
    recovered), other cabinet members, and Grant.

Q: Who accompanied President and Mrs. Lincoln to the theatre on April 14, 1865?

Q: What was the name of the play Lincoln was attending when Booth shot him? What was the name of the theatre?

Q: What words did John Wilkes Booth cry out when he jumped to the stage after shooting the president?

A: In place of several cancellations, Major Henry Rathbone (an administrative officer), and his fiancée, Clara Harris (a senator's daughter), were the Lincolns' companions.

A: *Our American Cousin*, a British comedy, was playing at Ford's Theatre, in Washington, D.C.

A: "Sic semper tyrannis!," which is Latin for "thus ever to tyrants," and is the motto of the state of Virginia.

IX. THE HOLY TEXT OF PIKE AND GUN

Q: With what ancient weapon did John Brown intend to arm the slaves he planned to free?

Q: What did the government manufacture at Harpers Ferry that attracted John Brown's attention?

Q: What did Union troops call their cheap uniforms that fell apart in heavy rains?

Q: What were "abatis"?

Q: Where was the Gatling gun used during the war?

Q: Where was the largest Civil War cannon?

Q: Who was the South's chief ordnance officer for the entire war?

Q: What did the Rains brothers do for the South?

A: Pikes. He brought about 1000 with him to Harpers Ferry.

A: The Model 1841 U.S. rifle (the "Mississippi Rifle") and the 1855 U.S. rifle musket.

A: "Shoddies." They were made from wool scraps.

A: Obstacles of trees with bent or sharpened branches that were directed towards the enemy to slow their advance.

A: This rapid-fire weapon was invented in the early 1860s, briefly used at Petersburg in 1864, but not perfected in time for significant service in the Civil War.

A: A 20-inch gun was mounted in Fort Hamilton, New York, but fired only in practice.

A: Josiah Gorgas. Given the Union blockade and the lack of domestic materials, he was surprisingly successful at keeping the South armed.

A: General Gabriel Rains developed the use of mines. Colonel George Washington Rains developed the world's largest gunpowder factory in Augusta, Georgia.

Q: Which were the most widely used revolvers in the Civil War?

Q: Which were the most widely used rifles in the war?

Q: What was the workhorse cannon on both sides?

Q: From what unusual vantage point did Thaddeus Lowe observe the Battle of Fair Oaks (June 4, 1862)?

Q: What was the problem with the Model 1855 Colt repeating rifle?

Q: What shape was the Minié ball?

Q: Why was this revolutionary bullet so deadly?

Q: What were the materials used to make cartridges for the Sharps carbine?

A: The Model 1860 Colt ("the new model") and the .44-caliber Remington.

A: The Model 1861 and 1863 Springfield rifles.

A: The 12-pound Napoleon smoothbore, with a maximum range of 1,000 yards.

A: Aboard his balloon, the *Intrepid*. He was the Union's first "aeronaut."

A: It sometimes discharged all six chambers at once.

A: It was not a ball; it was a conical bullet made of soft lead with a hollow base and grease grooves around its body.

A: There are two reasons. Rifling (the use of spiral grooves in a gun barrel) produced better accuracy and greatly extended the range of the older smoothbore musket. Weapons using these rounds also could be fired several times before cleaning. Secondly, because it was made of soft lead that expanded when the round was fired, it broke apart as it hit flesh, causing more harm.

A: Paper or linen. Sometimes the Rebs cut up public documents to make them.

Q: What was the name of the deadly artillery ammunition comprised of cast-iron balls packed into tin cylinders?

Q: What weapon did the Nashville Plow Works make?

Q: What did Federal troops call the 13-inch, 17,000-pound mortar they used during the Siege of Petersburg?

Q: Who devised the tunneling method for the Union mine at Petersburg, Virginia?

Q: What did Confederates call "Quaker guns"?

Q: By what name did antislavery settlers in Kansas call their Sharps rifles?

A: Canister.

A: In an ironic twist on Isaiah 2:4 ("They shall beat their swords into plowshares . . ."), it made sabers for the Confederate cavalry.

A: "The Dictator."

A: Colonel Henry Pleasants, formerly a mining engineer.

A: Confederate soldiers cut, painted, and deployed huge logs to look like cannons, to deceive the Federals about their artillery strength.

A: "Beecher's Bibles," after Henry Ward Beecher, who pledged to buy and ship them there from Brooklyn.

X. VIRTUE AND VIGILANCE

Q: Who wrote *Hospital Sketches* about her service as a Civil War nurse in 1863?

Q: What was the greatest killer in the war?

Q: What was the most common medical complaint?

Q: What was the most widely prescribed and damaging drug?

Q: Were more wounds caused by artillery, bullets, or hand-to-hand combat?

Q: What group was organized after the war by Clara Barton, the celebrated Union nurse and funds-raiser?

Q: What did Civil War soldiers call their sewing kits?

Q: What South Carolina plantation aristocrat is the best known diarist of the Civil War?

Q: Mary Custis Lee, Robert E. Lee's wife, had another famous general in her family. Who was he?

X. VIRTUE AND VIGILANCE

A: Louisa May Alcott of *Little Women* fame. She contracted typhoid fever after only three weeks at a Union hospital.

A: Disease. Diseases, including dysentery, scurvy, typhoid, malaria, pneumonia, measles, smallpox, and diphtheria claimed twice as many soldiers as battle did.

A: Diarrhea, also known as the "Virginia Quickstep."

A: Calomel or mercurous chloride. It caused hideous short- and long-term problems, including chronic mercury poisoning, but cured little.

A: About ninety percent were caused by bullets, mostly the .58-caliber Minié ball. Approximately six percent of wounds were from artillery, roughly four percent from swords or bayonets.

A: The American Red Cross.

A: Housewives.

A: Mary Boykin Chestnut, who was the wife of a Confederate brigadier general.

A: George and Martha Washington were her grandparents. (The mansion at Arlington, Virginia came from her side of the family.)

Q: What woman said of her husband, "he did not know the arts of a politician and would not practice them if understood"?

Q: What Southern spy was known in France as "La Belle Rebelle"?

Q: Ellen Marcy, later to become General McClellan's wife, was proposed marriage by what other Civil War figure?

Q: What did Sherman do to the civilian population after the capture of Atlanta?

Q: What did he do to the city itself?

Q: What general's name has become a synonym for "prostitute"?

Q: Who was left behind when Jefferson Davis and his cabinet evacuated Richmond in April 1865?

Q: In whose Washington boarding house did John Wilkes Booth and his fellow conspirators meet?

A: Varina Davis, the wife of Jefferson Davis, the president of the Confederacy.

A: Belle Boyd, the saucy secret agent who was made a captain and honorary aide-de-camp by Stonewall Jackson for her exploits.

A: Ambrose P. Hill, who became one of Lee's top officers.

A: He forced thousands of them to evacuate. John Bell Hood said, "In the name of God and humanity I protest!"

A: He ordered about one third of it burned after the evacuation.

A: Legend connects Union General "Fighting Joe" Hooker with the ladies of the night he rounded up in Washington.

A: Among others, Lee's wife Mary, whose arthritis was so bad that she could not travel.

A: Mary Surratt's. Her guilt is still debated, but she was hanged in July 1865.

XI. GOVERNMENT OF THE PEOPLE

Q: To which party did Lincoln belong when he was elected to Congress in 1846?

Q: Who was "the Great Compromiser"?

Q: How did Congressman Preston S. Brooks of South Carolina respond to a denunciation of proslavery settlers by Massachusetts Senator Charles Sumner in 1856?

Q: By what nickname was Lincoln's rival and debate opponent, Stephen A. Douglas, known?

Q: Lincoln and Douglas shared what aspect of their legal training?

Q: Believing both secession and coercion to be unconstitutional, who was the weak president who preceded Lincoln?

Q: Which party's 1860 platform affirmed "the right of each state to order and control its own domestic institutions"?

XI. GOVERNMENT OF THE PEOPLE

A: He was a Whig. This party was formed in opposition to Andrew Jackson and in favor of high tariffs. The Whig party declined in the 1850s and Lincoln became a Republican.

A: Senator Henry Clay of Kentucky brokered several deals, including one in 1850 to permit California to enter the Union as a free state, while strengthening the Fugitive Slave Law at the same time.

A: Brooks caned Sumner into unconsciousness on the Senate floor. After the caning, admirers sent Brooks new canes.

A: Douglas, who was 5' 4", was known as "the Little Giant."

A: Both were lawyers, but neither attended law school.

A: James Buchanan. He blamed the secession crisis on agitation in the North.

A: The Republican Party platform. Despite that fact, when Lincoln was elected, the Southern states began to secede.

Q: Other than Lincoln and Douglas, who ran for president in 1860?

Q: What Southern governor was deposed when he tried to stop his state from seceding?

Q: Stephen Douglas died on June 3, 1861, likely of exhaustion. What had he been doing?

Q: How did Lincoln hold Maryland in the Union?

Q: What future Supreme Court Justice was a Union officer badly wounded at both Ball's Bluff and Antietam?

Q: Who replaced Jeb Stuart when the legendary Rebel cavalry commander died at the Battle of Yellow Tavern in May 1864?

Q: Who enacted the first draft in American history?

A: The Southern Democrats nominated John C. Breckinridge of Kentucky, and the Whigs nominated John Bell of Tennessee.

A: Sam Houston of Texas. Houston, who tried unsuccessfully to prevent the secession of Texas, was deposed in March 1861 when he refused to swear allegiance to the Confederacy.

A: At Lincoln's request he was touring the border states, urging his supporters to remain loyal to the Union.

A: He sent troops to occupy Baltimore, locked up the mayor and legislature, and kept them there for two months without trial until a Unionist legislature had been elected.

A: Oliver Wendell Holmes, Jr.

A: Wade Hampton, reputed to be the richest man in the South, was the second-in-command to Stuart, and led the cavalry corps after Stuart's death. Hampton was later a governor of South Carolina.

A: In 1862, the Confederate Congress, at the prodding of Jefferson Davis, required healthy white men from 18 to 35 to serve for three years. Many refused. The Union enacted a draft law the following year.

Q: Who was exempted from the draft?

Q: How much did it cost to buy an exemption from the Union draft of 1863?

Q: By the end of 1863 what percentage of the Rebel army was absent (with leave or without)?

Q: Who was the Union's overall commander in the West?

Q: Who was "Father Neptune"?

Q: Who was Cassius Marcellus Clay?

Q: Who was Lincoln's vice president during his first term?

Q: Who was his second VP?

A: Men who paid for substitutes or who owned twenty or more slaves were exempted. Some Southerners raised the cry of "rich man's war, poor man's fight."

A: Northerners could pay a "commutation fee" of $300—almost a year's salary for an unskilled laborer.

A: Forty percent.

A: Explorer John Charles Frémont, who had been the first Republican candidate for President in 1856. Lincoln thought him "the damndest scoundrel that ever lived, but in the infinite mercy of Providence . . . also the damndest fool."

A: Lincoln's secretary of the navy, Gideon Welles.

A: Cassius Marcellus Clay was a long-time abolitionist from Kentucky who became Lincoln's minister to Russia. (Boxing champion Muhammad Ali, who was born with the same name, later said that Cassius Marcellus Clay was his "slave name.")

A: Hannibal Hamlin of Maine.

A: Andrew Johnson, a long-time Democrat from Tennessee.

Q: In 1864 how long had it been since a president was re-elected?

Q: Who did the Democrats nominate for president in 1864?

Q: How did the Democratic candidate do?

Q: Who was Jeff Davis's vice president?

Q: What affliction did Davis have?

Q: Who was the only Jewish member of the Confederate cabinet?

Q: Which post-Civil War presidents had owned slaves?

Q: What future president bought his way out of service in the war?

Q: What wealthy Robber Barons bought their way out of the service?

Q: How were Confederate officers below the rank of brigadier chosen?

A: Thirty-two years. Andrew Jackson was re-elected in 1832, but Van Buren, William H. Harrison, Tyler, Polk, Taylor, Fillmore, Pierce, and Buchanan, all served only one term each. (Or less—Harrison and Taylor died in office.)

A: George B. McClellan.

A: McClellan carried only three states (New Jersey and the border states of Delaware and Kentucky). Lincoln was re-elected in an electoral landslide, 212 to 21.

A: Alexander Stephens, who thought Davis was "weak and vacillating, timid, petulant, peevish, obstinate."

A: He was blind in his left eye.

A: Judah P. Benjamin served consecutively as attorney general, secretary of war and secretary of state.

A: Both Andrew Johnson and Ulysses S. Grant.

A: Grover Cleveland.

A: J. P. Morgan and Andrew Carnegie.

A: They were elected by the troops.

Q: What were "Copperheads"?

Q: What were "carpet-baggers"?

Q: Who was James Buchanan's vice president?

Q: Who was the last U.S. president to have served in the Civil War?

Q: Who else was in his unit?

Q: Which presidents served in the Civil War?

A: It was a pejorative term for Northerners who sympathized with the South, some of whom represented the peace faction of the Democratic Party.

A: Northerners who went to the South after the war to take advantage of the disruption by seeking political office. They were named after the manner in which some carried their belongings.

A: John Breckinridge was Buchanan's pro-slavery vice president, who became the presidential nominee for the pro-slavery wing of the Democratic Party in the 1860 election. He attempted to have his home state of Kentucky secede from the Union, but without success.

A: William McKinley, president from 1897–1901, rose from private to major in the 23rd Ohio.

A: Future President Rutherford B. Hayes, who was wounded four times and was once erroneously reported dead.

A: Six future presidents served in the Union army, none for the Confederacy. They were: Ulysses S. Grant, Rutherford B. Hayes, James A. Garfield, Chester A. Arthur, Benjamin Harrison, and William McKinley.

XII. NEVER FORGET WHAT THEY DID HERE

Q: Who is the villainous overseer in Harriet Beecher Stowe's *Uncle Tom's Cabin*?

Q: Rioters in Baltimore fired on Union troops in 1861. What journalist urged that the city be "burned with fire and leveled to the earth and made an abode for owls and satyrs and a place for fishermen to dry their nets"?

Q: What great poet said that the Civil War "saved" him?

Q: What are the names of Walt Whitman's two famous poems on the death of Abraham Lincoln?

Q: What novelist gushed about General McClellan and his troops, "they believed in him, and *so did I*"?

Q: Union Major General Lewis Wallace is famous for being the author of what book?

XII. NEVER FORGET WHAT THEY DID HERE

A: Simon Legree.

A: Horace Greeley, of the *New York Tribune*.

A: Walt Whitman, who cared for thousands of sick and wounded Union soldiers.

A: "When Lilacs Last in the Dooryard Bloom'd" and "O Captain! My Captain!"

A: Nathaniel Hawthorne.

A: Lew Wallace is best known for being the author of an all-time best seller, *Ben Hur*. There have been two classic films based on his 1880 novel.

Q: Who was the keynote speaker when Lincoln gave his Gettysburg Address in 1863?

Q: How many is "four score and seven"?

Q: Which young officer, a veteran of Shiloh, Chickamauga, Chattanooga, and Sherman's March, later wrote *The Devil's Dictionary*?

Q: How did he define "diplomacy"?

Q: What European intellectual had a series of newspaper articles on the war published in the *New York Daily Tribune*?

Q: What is the name of the young soldier at the center of Stephen Crane's *Red Badge of Courage*?

Q: Who wrote "What like a bullet can undeceive!"?

A: Edward Everett (1794–1865), a noted orator. He spoke for two hours; Lincoln spoke for five minutes.

A: Eighty-seven.

A: Ambrose Bierce (1842–1914), who served with the 9th Indiana Volunteers.

A: "The patriotic art of lying for one's country."

A: Karl Marx wrote these in 1861 and 1862 for the *New York Daily Tribune*. They were also published as *The Civil War in the United States* by Marx and Friedrich Engels.

A: Henry Fleming.

A: Herman Melville in his poem "Shiloh, A Requiem." Although the novelist did not serve in the war, he was deeply effected by it. His 1866 *Battle-Pieces and Aspects of the War* is perhaps his most powerful book of poetry.

Q: Where is the real Tara, on which the mansion in *Gone With The Wind* is based?

Q: What poet wrote a six-volume biography of Lincoln?

Q: In which novel did William Faulkner say that every Southern boy can picture himself at Gettysburg?

Q: Which are the last two states to use the Confederate battle emblem (the "Stars and Bars") on their own flags?

Q: What are some of the other names by which the Civil War is known?

Q: Which Union general has been falsely credited with the early development of baseball?

Q: Who held a séance in the White House during the Civil War?

A: There is no real Tara; it's a fiction of Margaret Mitchell's imagination.

A: Carl Sandburg (1878–1967) whose Illinois boyhood neighbors had known the late president.

A: *Intruder in the Dust* (1948).

A: Georgia and Mississippi.

A: The War Between (Against) the States, The Lost Cause, The War Against (of) Northern Aggression, The Brothers' War, The Second American Revolution, The Late Unpleasantness, The War of the Rebellion, The War of Attempted Secession.

A: General Abner Doubleday. He may not have invented baseball, but as a captain at Fort Sumter in 1861, Doubleday commanded the gunners that fired the first Union shots in retaliation.

A: Mary Todd Lincoln, the President's wife.

Q: Which baseball commissioner was named after a Civil War battle?

Q: What famous portrait photographer took few, if any, of the Civil War photos attributed to him?

Q: Which 1915 Civil War movie served both to create a vast national audience for film and to perpetuate virulently racist sentiments?

Q: What Edward Zwick movie depicts the 54th Massachusetts, the first regiment of black troops organized in a Northern state?

Q: Who sang a medley he called "American Trilogy," consisting of "Dixie," "Battle Hymn of the Republic," and the slave spiritual, "All My Trials"?

A: Kennesaw Mountain Landis (1866–1944) was named for the battle where his father, as a Union soldier, was wounded in 1864.

A: Mathew B. Brady. He was nearly blind by then, and his assistants took the pictures.

A: D. W. Griffith's *Birth of a Nation*.

A: *Glory* (1989), starring Matthew Broderick, Denzel Washington and Morgan Freeman.

A: Elvis Presley.

XIII. NOT PERISH FROM THE EARTH

Q: What did they do after the war?
1. William T. Sherman
2. Joshua L. Chamberlain
3. Andrew Johnson
4. Judah P. Benjamin
5. Henry Rathbone and Clara Harris,
   Lincoln's guests at Ford's Theatre

Q: Did immigrants still come to America during the Civil War?

Q: What Civil War veteran murdered and ate his companions on a doomed winter mining expedition in the Rockies in 1873?

Q: Wilmer McLean moved his family to safety far away from Bull Run in the summer of 1861, in advance of the first great battle of the Civil War. Where did they go?

XIII. NOT PERISH FROM THE EARTH

A: 1. He followed Grant as head of the army, but refused to go into politics.
2. He became Governor of Maine and President of Bowdoin College.
3. He succeeded Lincoln and was the first president to be impeached in 1868.
4. He fled to the Bahamas, then England, where he became Queen's Counsel.
5. They married and moved to Germany, where Rathbone went insane and murdered his wife.

A: Yes, about 800,000 did, mostly to the North from Germany (29%), Ireland (25%), and England (11%).

A: Alfred Packer served in the Union army and was discharged twice. He was accused of cannibalism and convicted of manslaughter in Colorado. The judge reportedly said, "They was seven Democrats in Hinsdale County and you, you voracious, man-eatin' son-of-a bitch, you ate five of 'em!"

A: They moved to Appomattox Court House, Virginia, where Lee surrendered to Grant in McLean's new house four years later. McLean said, "The war began in my front yard and ended in my front parlor."